SUNDAY EXPRESS & DAILY EXPRESS
CARTOONS

Eleventh Series

A DAILY EXPRESS PUBLICATION

Published by Beaverbrook Newspapers Limited, Fleet Street, London, E.C.4, and printed by Purnell and Sons, Ltd., Paulton (Somerset) and London

4/6

" Relax, bud,
it's one of
ours "

Daily Express, Oct. 9th, 1957

. . . . . selecting as a frontispiece
to the present volume, Giles'
famous cartoon that marked
the big event of the year—
the arrival of the Russian
satellite and the beginning of
The Space Age

FEELTHY GILES CARTOON?

(WITH CAPTION BY NASSER)

Yesterday's news that Nasser was reprinting *Daily Express* cartoons with captions altered to the pro-Nasser line brought mixed feelings to this department.

First reaction was to rush in to the editor and demand a wage increase, but reading on and coming to the piece which went: "In some cases the Arab caption writer may have been making an honest attempt to translate an untranslatable English joke" made us pause.

Loose remarks like this are apt to make a sensitive editor start asking why he has been paying us all these years for untranslatable jokes.

A suggestion to flout the Nasser caption writers was that all future cartoons published in the Express should be printed with 100 per cent pro-Nasser captions in the hope that in translation Nasser might find himself handing the Arabs a 100 per cent line of British propaganda.

However, until a retaliation campaign has been decided on, the examples below show what is going on. The original caption is printed in heavy type with the Nasser translation below.

"My damn feet are playing up Old Harry."

Translation
"Soon the little boots I will put on and kick the feelthy British out of Suez."

Daily Express, Aug. 28th, 1956

"Oh, dear, this is the 53rd cold this summer."

Translation
"Oh, dear, I hope Colonel Nasser doesn't stop smelling salts and aspirins coming through the Canal."

"I want my dinner."
Translation
"We want Nasser."

(Income Tax people please note: So far we have received no payment from Nasser)

"She's not as pretty as the waitress who served us at the Food Fair."

Daily Express, Aug. 30th, 1956

"Nasser's not the only one who needs to be advertising for pilots."

Sunday Express, Sept. 2nd, 1956

"Careful, boys—look where you're going."

Daily Express, Sept. 6th, 1956

"Pity you've got to rush back—I'd have liked you to have seen some more of our 'feather-bed' farming."

Sunday Express, Sept. 9th, 1956

"We KNOW you ain't showing Rock 'n' Roll. That's why we're coming in to bust the joint."

Daily Express, Sept, 13th, 1956

"Steward, who's piloting us these extra five thousand miles round the Cape—Stirling Moss?"

Sunday Express, Sept. 16th, 1956

If the Army Helps

"Drat 'im and 'is 'arvest 'elp and 'is ONE-TWO-ONE-TWO!"

Daily Express, Sept. 18th, 1956

"This Nasser certainly piloted that Clean-up-the-vice campaign off the front page."

Daily Express, Sept. 20th, 1956

"Wake up, Sleeping Beauty. We have information for thee."

Sunday Express, Sept. 23rd, 1956

"Well, you certainly found your place for a few quiet days away from Nassers and Liberaces"

Sunday Express, Sept. 30th, 1956

Daily Express, Oct. 5th, 1956

"Listen, Dai. When we've got them nicely tied up on Suez, Cyprus, wages, cost of living, you stand up and start hollering Home Rule for Wales."

Sunday Express, Oct. 7th, 1956

"Fifty to one against selling these cowboys tickets for Liberace OR Bolshoi."

Daily Express, Oct. 9th, 1956

B

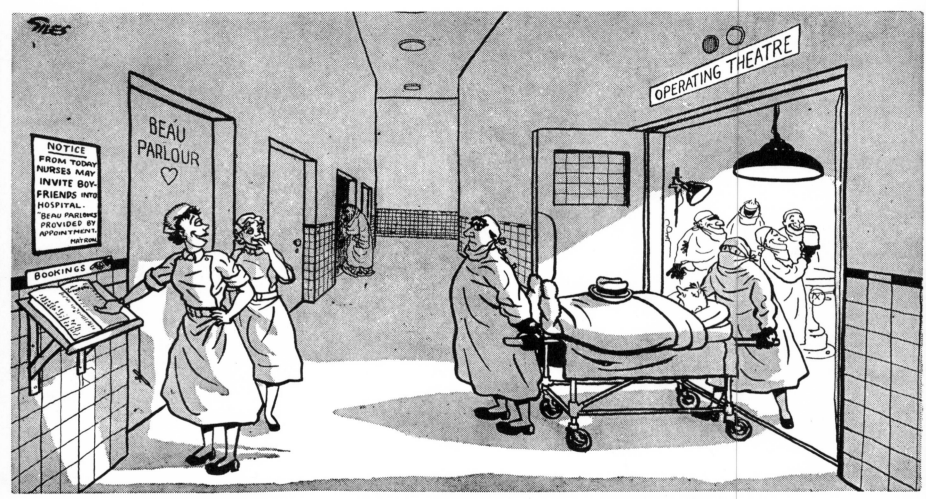

"You've done the wrong one. That's Sister's boy friend—he only called to say 'Good night'."

Daily Express, Oct. 16th, 1956

" 'Well,' I said, 'I'm fed up and want to go home,' and this sailor said, 'England expects every man to do his duty, chum,' and I said, 'Nelson wasn't always so hot at doing what he was told, chum,' then he flipped me one, then I flipped him one. . . ."

Sunday Express, Oct. 21st, 1956

**POSTSCRIPT
TO YESTERDAY'S
HAPPY REPORT THAT**

Daily Express, Oct. 23rd, 1956

● Princess Margaret, after being shown her room by Sir Evelyn Baring, introduced the rock 'n' roll language to Kenya by saying to him: "See you later, alligator." He smiled a little wanly and later asked his aide-de-camp what does "See you later, alligator" mean? His aide said he didn't know and was told to find out. Later he returned to tell Sir Evelyn that "You must reply: 'In a while, crocodile.'"

British Bwanas, determined not to be caught on the hop like Sir Evelyn, have arranged for experts on the language to be imported into Kenya as instructors.

**(MORE
OR LESS
OFFICIAL)**

"He's hiding in my tree."

Daily Express, Oct. 26th, 1956

"This patient has had fourteen prescriptions in

Sunday Express,

two days—we suspect him of hoarding."

Oct. 28th, 1956

—NOT FORGETTING THE MAN WHO MATTERS QUITE A LOT

"No one would ever convince my missus we were out there *fighting* them."

Daily Express, Nov. 1st, 1956

As Eden says, "This is not a state of war, simply armed conflict."

Sunday Express, Nov. 4th, 1956

POLITICS... THE GILES TOUCH

"On guard, men—severe case of politics just coming in."

Daily Express, Nov. 6th, 1956

"Once more round the block, O loved ones. We've got to use the damn stuff up somehow."

Sunday Express, Nov. 11th, 1956

PERSONAL CAMPAIGN

...BY GILES

—WITH APOLOGIES TO MR. BASIL CARDEW'S CYCLING CAMPAIGN

Today the Boot and Shoe Makers' Association (supported by the Arts Council) announces a brilliant decision.

The decision: to produce a little booklet to be given away free to every motorist about to be deprived of his petrol.

It is the industry's answer to the growing concern that now most people have two or three cars each they have forgotten how to walk.

I estimate that several million copies of the book will be circulated at a cost of many tens of thousands of pounds.

The book will be divided into two parts. The first half will be written in simple terms to appeal to the child who gets a new cycle to watch out for motorists learning to walk; the second half will be advice on first aid.

Experts from the Boot and Shoe Makers' Association will write the book. Let **ME**—as an old campaigner for motorists' safety—give **THEM** some advice.

... HOW 'TIS DONE :

THE WALK ... AND THE RUN

THE WALK: 1. Stand dead still for 40 minutes or so with both feet firmly on the ground. (Use sticks if necessary).

2. Raise left foot a little way off the ground.

3. Bring left foot forward remembering to keep right foot on the ground.

4. Lower left foot gently to the ground.

5. Pause.

6. Pick yourself up and have another go.

7. If you have not gone down again by the time you get to position 5 raise *right* foot a little way off the ground.

8. Bring right foot forward remembering to keep left foot on the ground.

9. Lower right foot gently to the ground. You should now be ready for position 1 again. Repeat 1, 2, 3, 4, 5, 6, 7, 8, 9, 1, 2, 3, 4, 5, 6, 7, 8, 9, 1, 2, 3, 4, 5, 6, 7, 8, 9, and see how many times you get knocked head-over-driving-seat between your house and the office.

* * *

THE RUN: This is the same workout as the walk only faster, but should not be attempted by motorists who smoke more than 80 a day, or under the influence of drink.

I forecast that pedestrian crossings will be packed to capacity as motorists are the only people who know what they're for.

Daily Express, Nov. 13th, 1956

"These yours? We found them stowed away in the Trans-Antarctic expedition ship."

Daily Express, Nov. 15th, 1956

"Who's been playing blocking canals and sinking ships in my bath?"

Sunday Express, Nov. 18th, 1956

"Ike's fixed my Anglo-American relationship for keeps if petrol shortage means goodbye Cadillacs."

Daily Express, Nov. 22nd, 1956

"Don't mind us—we're the Canal Users Association."

Sunday Express, Nov. 25th, 1956

Neatest Nothing-to-do-with-Nasser story was surely the announcement that the nudists of Britain are urging an M.P. to take up their cause. "Wanted"—said the headline—"Nudist M.P." There were cries of "Oh, I say," "Oi, oi," and "Order, please" when the new M.P. entering the Commons turned out to be a lady.

Daily Express, Nov. 27th, 1956

c

"I guess that'll take care of the dear boy's Yuletide motoring."

Daily Express, Nov. 30th, 1956

"Bought them two gallons of beer for a gallon of petrol, then they said, 'Help yourself from the front of our truck.' "

Daily Express, Dec. 4th, 1956

"First Sunday I've had off since I opened this garage

Sunday Express,

so I thought I'd run the family down to the coast."

Dec. 2nd, 1956

"When a poor man came in sight . . . Gathering winter fu-el."

Daily Express, Dec. 6th, 1956

"Bought her a coffee in Port Said and she's followed me around ever since."

Sunday Express, Dec. 9th, 1956

"Decorations are an essential part of the gaiety of Christmas . . . the whole family is drawn closer together by the fragile links of a paper chain."—*Daily Express*, yesterday.

Daily Express, Dec. 13th, 1956

The Last Word on Petrol

Daily Express, Dec. 18th, 1956

"His Royal Highness—King of the Office Parties—home bang on time as usual to help with the decorations."

Sunday Express, Dec. 23rd, 1956

P.S. To that Contest

"I should take your little joke off the wall—here comes your missus."

Daily Express, Dec. 24th, 1956

"Come and say 'Good morning' to what you called 'The sweetest Christmas present you have had'."

Daily Express, Dec. 27th, 1956

"Honest, Dad, there was tons of snow here yesterday."

Sunday Express, Dec. 30th, 1956

"Off home, all of you, before I charge you with being dressed in a manner likely to cause a breach of the peace."

Daily Express, Jan. 1st, 1957

"I believe you deliberately ran out of petrol so you could sail it home."

Daily Express, Jan. 4th, 1957

"Someone must have told this son of a sheik we were coming, sergeant."

"But, Sir, surely you bought *your* Empire for a few strings of beads."

Daily Express, Jan. 8th, 1957

"If you be so hot on politics why weren't you messing off up to Lunnun while there were a vacancy?"

Sunday Express, Jan. 13th, 1957

"Five new arrivals, Sir. Whole-heartedly endorse Mr. Macmillan's economy drive, ask would it help if they resigned?"

Daily Express, Jan. 17th, 1957

Following the announcement that Rommel's ex-chief of staff, Lieut.-General Speidel, is to command the British Army of the Rhine. . . .

Sunday Express, Jan. 20th, 1957

The Police started something when they fined a man £1 this week for looking after someone else's dog and not holding a licence, although the owner had one. The discovery of this law places people like kennel owners, British Railways, etc., in a funny position. You and all, Constable.

Daily Express, Jan. 22nd, 1957

"BANG! BANG! BANG! BANG! I had a new baby brother this morning."

Sunday Express, Jan. 27th, 1957

The announcement that women may now study at Oxford in unlimited numbers was welcomed by most male undergrads. "But," said a well-known warden to a don, "kindly explain to little Miss Whatsit that such studies as boat-racing, the placing of utensils on spires, the debagging of Principals, were always—and shall remain—the undisputed privileges of the Male."

Daily Express, Feb. 1st, 1957

"Kindly remove thy hand from knee, O Major. We ain't dolls, we're F.B.I."

Sunday Express, Feb. 3rd, 1957

"I thought I told you to stay out of sight while the judges were around."

Sunday Express, Feb. 10th, 1957

"Now if Private Wilson had referred to his little regulations book he would have observed there are certain items acquired whilst on overseas service which one is not allowed to take back to the United Kingdom."

Sunday Express, Feb. 17th, 1957

"Boy, go tell your mother it's the landlord called about the new rent increase."

Daily Express, Feb. 19th, 1957

"MANSION 'OUSE!!! GIT a move on, some of yer. . . . Beg pardon, your Royal Highness—didn't see you in there"

Daily Express, Feb. 26th, 1957

No joke, no political motive. Simply an illustration to yesterday's fascinating headline: M.P.s IN PARIS BEG FOR A MEAL.

Daily Express, Feb. 28th, 1957

"What shall we do with the redundant sailor . . ."

Daily Express, Mar. 7th, 1957

"Today's the Ides of March."

Daily Express, Mar. 15th, 1957

"You've read about that farmer who objected to a pylon on his land so he

Sunday Express,

knocked it down? Well, that goes for me and that damn' gasworks."

"A Reverend Shop Steward to see you, Your Grace."

Sunday Express, Mar. 17th, 1957

"Never mind about it being time you knocked off for your token strike—pass me that ———— spanner."

Daily Express, Mar. 21st, 1957

GRANDMA GILES CALYPSO

Said Mac to Ike we'd better get back
Or like another P.M. we'll be getting the sack.
Said Ike to Mac if you take my tip,
You'll go by plane and not by ship.

For the ocean liners have to roll and rock
And let 'emselves into Southampton Dock.
The meeting ended as a great success
Now Selwyn and Mac are back in the mess.

(Chorus, if you like)

But it was well worth going all those thousands of
miles,
For Uncle Sam is sending us some Guided Missiles.
Said a shipyard worker laughing fit to bust
You won't see my heels for Atom Dust.

(With apologies to Cy Grant and the B.B.C.)

HERE is the news of Selwyn and Mac,
They've been to Bermuda and now they're back.
They went to tell Ike that they like Ike,
And forget all about the Shipyard Strike.

CHORUS

We bring you the news that you ought to know
In today's tropical Calyp-so.
They talked all day in the Bermuda sun
While the folk back home were having their fun
Losing their money on the week's big race
With strikes breaking out all over the place.

Colonel Nasser he demand more pay.
Makarios will be home any day.
Everyone'll listen to what he sez
About us and our restrictive pract-i-ces.

(Chorus)

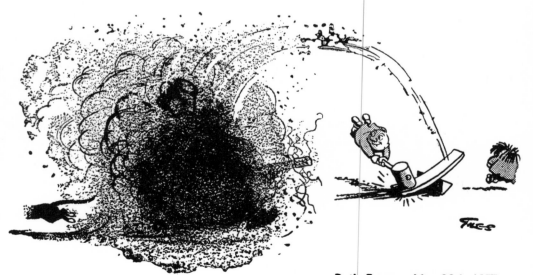

Daily Express, Mar. 28th, 1957

"Sad, really, pinching his flars and selling 'em to him for Mother's Day."

Sunday Express, Mar. 31st, 1957

"You're just like this stuff they're going to send us from the States—guided missiles with no ——— heads."

Sunday Express, April 7th, 1957

"1944 is the long time—but always I say 'My Basilkins, one day 'e come back.' "

Daily Express, April 9th, 1957

"Why's Dad trying to book a single reservation on the Mayflower?"

Sunday Express, April 14th, 1957

"It's full of carbide and heavy water."

Daily Express, April 18th, 1957

"When I said 'For better or worse' yesterday I hadn't seen that hat."

Sunday Express, April 21st, 1957

"This one's mine—send him home with a Tony Curtis if you dare."

Daily Express, April 24th, 1957

British advertisements in America invite the tourist to our shores where, they say, he will meet "fascinating and genial people" even in railway compartments.

In case the prospective tourist may be a little mystified by the many brands of "fascinating and genial people" to be found over here this illustration of a typical British scene is numbered with references to help the visitor to recognise just how fascinating and genial we really are.

Nos. 1, 2, 3, 4 and 5 are the fascinating and genial people with whom he has just spent a long unfascinating train journey in icy silence.

No. 6. Will help the visitor to appreciate that the British are inclined to be somewhat "doggie" and, contrary to popular belief, drive on the same side of the road as they do in the States.

No. 7. That we are also very fond of pussy.

No. 8. This fascinating, genial gentleman should be treated with a certain amount of caution. He is liable to guide you on your way with the usual "keep-straight-on-you-can't-miss-it" and set you back a few dollars.

No. 9. Oldest inhabitant. Don't be fascinated by this type at any cost. He'll put the bite on you for the lot.

No. 10. Landlord of Ye Old Hospitable British Inn. Try asking him for beer on ice and be fascinated by his warm reply.

No. 11. Avoid this one more than the oldest inhabitant. He's the equivalent to the Eastern gentleman who trades rude postcards, only he plugs you with endless unfunny stories about an Englishman, an Irishman, and a Scotsman, and carries wads of unfascinating poems scrawled on the backs of grimy envelopes.

No. 12. Known to the natives as the "Bar Parlour". You're in luck. It's shut except on Sundays.

No. 13. Fascinating and genial railway porter saying it's about toim he were getting back as he believes he dew hear a plagy train acumin.

No. 14. One of your countrymen in the service has just passed this way.

No. 15. Fascinating and genial arm of the law.

No. 16. Notice telling you that all future trains are either cancelled or going to be late.

No. 17. Poster telling you to spend your holiday in the States.

No. 18. Poster telling you how to emigrate.

No. 19. Well, if you like ye fascinating "Dainty Teas" . . .

No. 20. You're in luck again. They're closed for lunch.

Good Day . . . Dydd Da . . . Guid Mornin' . . . Top o' the Mornin' . . .

Daily Express, April 22nd, 1957

"Tough luck, boys—your ship going off in a hurry like that."

Sunday Express, April 28th, 1957

"As far as I can make out he wishes to trade you six of his wives and a camel for a carton of Lucky Strike."

Daily Express, May 1st, 1957

"Parked on a bus stop so we roped him in."

Daily Express, May 3rd, 1957

"Same with mine—she didn't know I had a tonsil in me head till Prince Charles's made headlines this week."

F

Sunday Express, May 12th, 1957

"Having got supplementary coupons for running my wife's poor old mother around for her health, the end of rationing presents a bit of a problem."

Daily Express, May 15th, 1957

"In the absence of His Royal Highness I shall endeavour to instil learning by the less spectacular but well-proven methods.
Come out the boy who wrote this patriotic message."

Daily Express, May 21st, 1957

Not least among the week's great headlines was the official announcement that women Wolf Cub leaders may now wear shorts, with a request that "they should be utilitarian rather than ornamental".

Sunday Express, May 26th, 1957

"Certainly not, Edward. We might like it."

Daily Express, May 28th, 1957

"I dare you."

Daily Express, May 30th, 1957

"The management regrets that your premium bond and the chance of your horse being in the first three on Wednesday is insufficient security for another pint on the slate."

Sunday Express, June 2nd, 1957

"The President of the Peace Loving Movement then added that Russia's latest H-bomb, if dropped on the North Pole, was capable of melting all the snow and ice, which would flood London in a matter of minutes. Which wouldn't do that cold of yours any good, Vera."

Daily Express, June 4th, 1957

"Certainly they're mine. Finest team of Welsh sheep dogs that ever came to London, mun."

Daily Express, June 10th, 1957

"I see they had

to tow it in."

Daily Express, June 14th, 1957

"Never mind about it being

past the longest day—'op it."

Sunday Express, June 23rd, 1957

"Of course, you realise that if my Dad gives it up we shall have to start buying our own."

Sunday Express, June 30th, 1957

"What the hell were you two celebrating Independence Day for, anyway?"

Daily Express, July 5th, 1957

"How about reducing my charges as I've got a three-guinea rise in the House of Lords? Certainly not."

Sunday Express, July 7th, 1957

An appeal has been made for every nurse to be off duty during the inquiry into the Nurses *v.* Hospital Authorities dispute in Guernsey.

Daily Express, July 16th, 1957

G

"Boy—with their regular bus on strike, are they glad to see me. Raise your 'at to 'em as we go by."

Sunday Express, July 21st, 1957

"Ethel—I'll cycle to work for the duration of the strike without a murmur. But don't keep telling me it'll do me good."

Daily Express, July 23rd, 1957

"Pity we couldn't squeeze another one in—that was my wife."

Daily Express, July 25th, 1957

"In the words of the poet—someone hath blundered."

Sunday Express, July 28th, 1957

Letter from a cow

Sir:

On behalf of all the cows in Britain I cannot protest too strongly against the proposal that the Milk Publicity Council should use "glamorised cows" on the hoardings in place of the drink-more-milk girl—Zoe Newton.

It is stated that a branch of the Housewives' League has said: "Let's publicise the animals that produce the milk. We breed the finest cows in the world," and added that they (the wives) did not think Zoe Newton was attractive and nor did their husbands.

Which is just a lot of bull's eye.

The real reason they want Zoe off the hoardings is because they know very few husbands drink milk, and that wistful expression as they gaze starry-eyed at the posters is for Zoe Newton and not the product she is tempting you to buy.

We fully sympathise with the Housewives' League's concern that Miss Newton is inadvertently stealing their husbands' affections, but must remind them that if pictures of "glamorised cows" are to be used instead, we shall be faced with the same concern as the Housewives' League.

A "glamorised cow" on a hoarding is bound to prove more attractive to our weak-minded husband than us, his less glamorised, over-worked wives.

And for the benefit of editors and some town people who may not appreciate that herds of cows have only one husband between the lot of them I wish to state that any additional competition such as "glamorised cows" on hoardings would be most unwelcome.

We would remind the Milk Publicity Council that if they go ahead with this new line in advertising they will not only be doing us a great disservice, but will also be doing themselves one.

For even they must realise that the milk yield from a "glamorised cow" on a hoarding is pretty low, and ours will be just about as low if our husbands' affections are to be lured away by these painted, paper dolls.

Yours,

A SHORTHORN.

Daily Express, July 30th, 1957

Don't get your feet wet—

Before taking to the water beginners should study this and the next three cartoons. They not only introduce some of the basic types of the sailing world but demonstrate a few of the many perils to avoid.

Some of the finer points of sailing are not easy to illustrate, such as the class warfare between motor-boaters and sailing-boaters. But if the beginner doesn't know about this one he soon will.

Just as he will quickly catch on that there are no "Fronts" or "Backs", "Lefts" or "Rights". In sailing language everything is "Aft" about "Forrud" and "Starbud" and "Portsud".

This first cartoon illustrates a very great "DON'T" to motor-boaters at Cowes this week.

Daily Express, Aug. 5th, 1957

Don't on any account offer members of the Royal Yacht Squadron a tow
should they appear to be a little on the drag in a race

Daily Express, Aug. 5th, 1957

1, 2, 3, 4 and 5. Crew. Ocean-going type.

6. Crew. Naval escort type.

7. Owner-driver type.

8. Uncle Harold and Auntie Mary, R.N. Retired. (Uncle Harold of course, not Auntie Mary).

9 and 10. "Know-the-lot" types.

11. We haven't quite got the hang of things yet.

12. "I hope you haven't forgotten anything, Henry."

13. Me taking to the water.

14. Boat and crew aft up-'ards.

15. Boat and crew nearly aft up'ards.

16. Lugsail-only type.

17. This type of yacht is not recommended for beginners.

18. Land race watching yacht race with enthusiasm.

Daily Express, Aug. 6th, 1957

Daily Express, Aug. 7th, 1957

IMPORTANCE OF DRESS

This should really have been the first lesson, but if it is not too late take my advice and ignore the popular misconception that life on the water is free and easy and that you can wear any old thing you like. In this illustration of a typical sailing club bar only one man is improperly dressed.

Daily Express, Aug. 7th, 1957

CONCLUDING this short series introducing beginners to the waterfront I
quote: "There is nothing—absolutely nothing—guaranteed to buck you up more
than simply messing about in boats."

Daily Express, Aug. 8th, 1957

"There'll be some hollering when we get in—I locked Grandma in the bathroom before we went away."

Sunday Express, Aug. 11th, 1957

"Same goes for this stuff as Scotch during Prohibition. Peddling it to the natives is illegal."

Daily Express, Aug. 28th, 1957

"I suppose Tom is what you call dressed in the height of fashion."

Sunday Express, Sept. 1st, 1957

The Last Word on the Sack

"Men are all the same—no fashion sense whatsoever."

Daily Express, Sept. 5th, 1957

"36, 23, 34. We've switched from engine spotting since we read the Wolfenden Committee's report on vice."

Sunday Express, Sept. 8th, 1957

"I'd show him who's favourite in this house if they ever let him out for a fly round the room."

Sunday Express, Sept. 15th, 1957

"What do we do—get up there and bash 'em or pick it up?"

Daily Express, Sept. 19th, 1957

Off on a matter far and away from the monetary meetings and the Bank rate. Over to a subject filed under "Opportunities too good to be missed"—the address by my Lord Beaverbrook to the Canadian Education Association the other day.

At the risk of receiving six of the best from the Head (Lord B) I wish to state that his entire speech was nothing but a lot of first-class propaganda put over for the benefit of the enemy. The enemy, so far as this department is concerned, being anybody remotely connected with education or even resembling a schoolteacher.

The only good that may come of Lord B's praise of teachers is that he probably flattered them into a feeling of false security which can only lead them to disaster

Cross-section of harvest left to nature . . .

Lord B told the Education Association that "grasp and understanding of humanity" makes a successful teacher.

The only teacher I ever knew who allowed himself to be lulled into thinking he had "grasp and understanding of humanity" forgot to lash out at us with his canes and rulers one day and was therefore considered easy prey by us, the pupils, who from then on gave him the old what-o till the end of his term of office.

I can see the schoolteachers' chests puffing out as Lord B told them: "You sow You cultivate. You drill and hoe. But you leave the harvest to nature."

Cultivators, drills, and hoes were about the only implements not used on us to guide us in the paths of learning, and a quick look-round at the "harvest left to nature" should return any schoolteacher's inflated chest to normal.

Daily Express, Sept. 25th, 1957

And to the adults who are for ever telling us that modern youth is degenerate, the "other forces" referred to by Lord B when he said: "Other specialists in education deal with the ripened grain" could only mean the police.

While I agree with Lord B's belief that the career of the educationist is "not the way of worldly gain, that the prizes are few and the hardships many", memories of some of my schooldays prompt me to say serve 'em right.

And I am certainly with him on his remark that: "Dull and pompous speeches breed illiteracy and promote slumber."

I'm not sure where I got my illiteracy, but the little scars on the the back of my head are reminders of many rude awakenings during dull and pompous speeches.

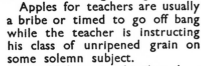

"Specialist" dealing with ripened grain

If I had been addressing the educationists I would not have boosted their ego by telling them about famous people of the past who were once schoolmasters—Carlyle, Clemenceau, James, Isaac Watts, and the rest. I would have made them alive to the dangers of their profession—the infamous pupils of the past and present.

The quiet one, for instance. The one no teacher can nail although he knows that this type is always the brain behind any upheaval in the class.

The pupils with eye half-closed making notes on a cigarette packet to be used as evidence in court when the pupil's mother brings a case against the teacher for gently telling her boy that he would prefer him not to throw his tapioca pudding at his teacher during free meal times.

I would have warned the educationists to be on guard against the apple-for-my-teacher brigade.

Apples for teachers are usually a bribe or timed to go off bang while the teacher is instructing his class of unripened grain on some solemn subject.

I could have taught them how to detect the arson types, the betting types, the future-editor types, the blackmailing types, the—but why should I give them the gleanings from the stockyard of my well mis-spent youth?

Instead, I will securely place in a strategic position a large volume, "Farming the Hard Way", published by H.M. Stationery Office, and wait calmly for a phone call from Lord B.

Promoted slumber . . .

Daily Express, Sept. 25th, 1957

... and so, dear Father, in view of the Chancellor's call for stringent economy I fear it would be incompatible with his request for me to advance you a small loan until Friday, even at the tempting offer of 7% interest. Your affectionate son ...

Sunday Express, Sept. 22nd, 1957

GILES IN AMERICA

"O.K., let's have it again. I'm the Queen standing on Park-avenue. Mulligan comes out of 52nd-street and pokes the side of your cab. Whadya say? No you don't. You say: 'Pardon me, Mulligan,' and Mulligan says: 'Pardon ME, Butch'." . . . .

Daily Express, Oct. 7th, 1957

WINDSOR WAFFLES $2.90

SANDRINGHAM SUNDAES $1.90

LIZ & PHIL SPECIAL $5.90

BALMORAL BIFSTAKE $2.90

ROYAL STAKE-BURGERS 90¢

ROYAL HAM & SWISS $2.75

ROYAL SWISS & HAM $2.75

Welcome LIZ & PHIL

CHEEP-EETS

REDS LAUNCH MOON

MAYOR TO DINE LIZ AT WALDORF

SERIES

N.Y. DATES FOR LIZ AND PHIL

LIZ TO

"Royal Buck Pal Special—hot dog and doughnuts to you, Mac."

Daily Express, Oct. 8th, 1957

"You'd think a royal visit and a baseball World Series was enough in one month."

Daily Express, Oct. 10th, 1957

"How in heck are we gonna make Satellite rhyme with Moon, June, Toon . . ."

Sunday Express, Oct. 13th, 1957

"I ain't kiddin' nobody—I ain't said Her Majesty's coming through Lower East. All I've said is New York's on the royal route."

Daily Express, Oct. 15th, 1957

"So teacher's 'How would you like a picnic out at Bronx Zoo, boys?' turns out to be a fix with the cops to get one security problem out of the way while the Queen is down-town."

Daily Express, Oct. 17th, 1957

"We're in at the banquet, Martha—I've got that job as waiter and you're the hat-check girl."

Daily Express, Oct. 18th, 1957

"Elmer! I don't give a damn how pro-Monarchist you are—take it off and take it back where you rented it at once."

Sunday Express, Oct. 20th, 1957